BRAIN TEASERS

This edition published in 2008 by Arcturus Publishing Limited
26/27 Bickels Yard, 151–153 Bermondsey Street,
London SE1 3HA

Copyright © 2007 Arcturus Publishing Limited

ISBN: 978-1-84193-777-9

Printed in China

Design & Illustration by quadrum■

BRAIN TEASERS

Capella

Contents

Memory Games

Test your memory! Look carefully at the following pictures then turn the page to answer some questions. No peeking!

Clowning Around!

Questions
Game - Page 5

1. What is the elephant playing?

2. How many hoops are there on the ground?

3. What is the bear riding?

4. How many giraffes are there in the box?

5. Is there a lion anywhere in the picture?

6. What is the rabbit holding in his paw?

7. How many parrots are there in the picture?

8. Does the mini train have any wheels?

Funtime At School!

Questions
Game - Page 7

1. How many boys are looking at the chart on the table?

2. What is the little boy holding up in his hand?

3. Is there a school bag lying on the ground?

4. How many girls are there in the picture?

5. Is anything lying on top of the book shelf?

6. Is there a round table in the picture?

7. How many chairs are there in the picture?

8. How many chairs have children sitting on them?

Couch Potato!

Questions
Game - Page 9

1. Is the girl wearing a hairband?

2. How many flowers are there in the painting on the wall?

3. Are there any pets in the room?

4. Is the girl sitting on the couch or the chair?

5. What are the items on the table?

6. Is there anything underneath the table?

7. Is the girl wearing slippers?

8. Are there any curtains in the window?

9. What is the girl holding in her left hand?

Take Your Pick!

Questions
Game - Page 11

1. How many customers are there in the showroom?

2. Is there a clock on the wall?

3. How many cars are there in the showroom?

4. Is there a glove on the table?

5. What is underneath the pen lying on the table?

6. How many people in the showroom are adults?

7. Do all the cars have rearview mirrors?

8. How many lights are there on the showroom ceiling?

Playing In The Park!

Questions
Game - Page 13

1. How many dogs are there in the park?

2. How many adults are there?

3. How many children are playing in the sand?

4. Is a girl or a boy coming down the slide?

5. How many park benches are there?

6. What is the man in the picture doing?

7. Is there a sign board visible anywhere?

8. Are there any birds in the sky?

9. How many children are wearing caps?

Hard At Work!

Questions
Game - Page 15

1. How many people are there in the office?

2. Is the man wearing glasses?

3. Is there a laptop anywhere in the office?

4. Is the dustbin by the table full or empty?

5. How many chairs are there in the picture?

6. Is there a clock on the wall?

7. Is there a mobile phone on any of the tables?

8. Does the woman have long hair or short hair?

9. Is there a couch in the room?

Sail Away!

Questions
Game - Page 17

1. How many people on the ship's deck are wearing hats?

2. How many birds are there in the sky?

3. Is the sun visible behind the clouds?

4. How many people are relaxing in the sun loungers?

5. How many people on the ship's deck are smoking?

6. Is there a porthole on the side of the ship?

7. How many lifebuoys are there on the side of the ship?

8. How many tables are there?

On The Farm!

Questions
Game - Page 19

1. How many pigs are there on the farm?

2. What is the farmer holding in his hand?

3. How many chicks are standing around the hen?

4. Is there a windmill in the picture?

5. Is there a bird sitting on the fence?

6. Is there a worm peeking out from a hole in the ground?

7. Does the house have a chimney?

8. How many cows are on the farm?

Shop 'Til You Drop!

Questions
Game - Page 21

1. How many watches are there in the case?

2. What is the girl wearing in her hair?

3. Is there a teddy bear anywhere?

4. How many shopping carts are there?

5. Does the girl have stripes on her shirt?

6. Is the girl wearing high heels?

7. Is a butterfly anywhere in the picture?

8. Are there any lights on the shop ceiling?

Santa's Here!

Questions
Game - Page 23

1. How many children are standing around Santa?

2. Are any of the children holding presents in their hands?

3. Are there any Santa hats lying on the ground?

4. How many balloons are decorating the ceiling?

5. How many buttons does Santa's suit have?

6. Is the Christmas tree decorated with candy canes?

7. Is Santa sitting or standing?

8. Is there any holly?

Number Fun

1. Up the Stairs

Joe started making a staircase out of his wooden blocks. This is what he did to make his staircase 3 steps high.

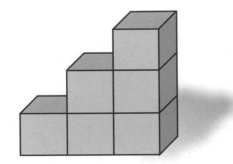

How many more blocks will he need if he wants to make it 9 steps high?

2. In Time for the Office

Mr Davies must reach his office everyday by 9 o'clock in the morning. He needs 15 minutes to get dressed and 20 minutes for his breakfast. The drive from his house to the office takes another 35 minutes. What is the latest time at which he must get up, so that he reaches his office on time?

3. Number Roundabout

Rebecca thinks of a one digit number. She multiplies it by 3, adds 8, divides by 2 and then subtracts 6. To her surprise she gets the same number that she had thought of in the first place. What is the number?

4. Summer School

Karen has a very busy day at summer school. She can never remember when each activity starts! This is what she remembers:

- Swimming is the last activity of the day.
- Music comes after Arts and Crafts and both will be before lunch.
- Dance is in the afternoon.

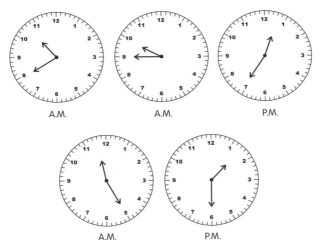

Can you match the times above to each of the activities: Swimming, Arts and Crafts, Music, Dance and lunchtime?

5. How many Sweets?

Amanda, Charlotte, Ingrid, Ronnie and Leona had 36 sweets in all.

- Each child had at least 5 sweets.
- Ingrid had 2 more sweets than Charlotte.
- Ronnie had twice as many sweets as Amanda.
- Leona had 3 sweets less than Ronnie.

How many sweets did each person have?

6. Mothers and Daughters

One day, two mothers and two daughters went shopping. They went to a shoe shop and bought shoes. Each bought a pair of shoes and altogether they bought 3 pairs of shoes. How is this possible?

7. Broken Eggs

Jamal bought a box of eggs and when he got home he realized that a quarter were broken. What percentage of the whole box was broken?

8. Drawing in Circles

Can you draw the figure given below following these rules?

- Once you begin, you cannot lift your pen or pencil from the paper.
- You cannot go over any line that has been already drawn.

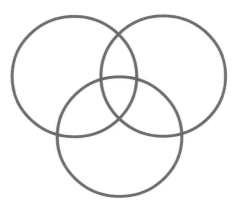

9. Book Club

Kersey and her three cousins, Amy, Jeanne, and Ron, decided to start a book club. Each of them contributed a certain number of books to the club. Together, Kersey and her cousins had 22 books. Half of the books belonged to Kersey. The rest were contributed by her cousins.

- Amy contributed 2 more books than Jeanne.
- Ron contributed 1 more book than Amy.

How many books did each child contribute to the book club?

10. Talking Telephones

The buttons on the telephone keypad have been given letters of the alphbet. Substituting each letter for its corresponding number, add up each word, then solve the sums given below.

a.   BUS

    + CAR

    ────────

    ────────

Telephone Keypad

1	2 ABC	3 DEF
4 GHI	5 JKL	6 MNO
7 PQRS	8 TUV	9 WXYZ
*	0	#

b.   LONDON

    - PARIS

    ────────

    ────────

c.   FAN

    x TV

    ────────

    ────────

d. I $\overline{)\text{CHIPS}}$ = ...

31

11. How Old Are They?

Mrs Smith has 6 daughters. Each daughter is 4 years older than her next younger sister. The oldest daughter is 3 times older than her youngest sister. How old is each of Mrs Smith's daughters?

12. Same Speed!

The two columns below show the distances travelled and journey times of 4 vehicles. Match the distance with the time each vehicle took if they were travelling at the same speed.

Distance (km)	Time (hrs)
280	7
350	9
630	4
490	5

What is their common speed in kilometres per hour?

13. Know Your Numbers

When writing all the whole numbers from (and including) 1 to 100, which digit will you write the LEAST number of times?

a. 0
b. 1

c. 5
d. 9

14. An Apple A Day

I have 90 apples. I give 10 apples to my friend and the rest I divide equally among 10 children. Each child gives one of their apples to my friend. How many apples does my friend have?

a. 20
b. 11
c. 10
d. 15

15. Average Age

The average age of Timothy and Terence is 11 yrs 5 months. Teresa is 10 yrs 8 months old. What is the average age of Timothy, Terence and Teresa?

16. Sally's Book

Sally read 38 pages of a book on Thursday afternoon. She read 27 more pages on Friday than she read on Thursday. But she still has 216 more pages left. How many pages are there in the book?

17. Where Are The Plus Signs?
In order to get a total of 99 from the following sequence of numbers, where will you need to put 6 plus signs?
987654321

18. Who Is The Oldest?
Jeremy is older than Kimberley and Kimberley is older than Sydney. Sydney is younger than Jeremy and Ruth is older than Jeremy. Put the names of these children in order, starting with the oldest and finishing with the youngest.

19. Final Destination
A truck travels at an average speed of 44 km per hour. It completes 1/3 of its journey in 40 minutes. What is the total distance that the truck must cover before it reaches its destination?

20. From London to Dover

Paul left London at 3.15 p.m. and reached Canterbury after 2 hours. The average speed at which he drove was 74 km/hr. Paul then took 40 minutes to drive from Canterbury to Dover. This time his average speed was 54 km/hr. What was Paul's average speed during his entire journey?

21. A Jug of Milk

If one quarter of a litre of milk is added to this jug that contains milk up to the mark shown, how much milk will there be in the jug?

22. Colour Correctly!

Joe has divided a circle into six identical parts as shown. How many of them should he colour if he wants to colour 25% of the circle? Get a coloured pencil and have a go!

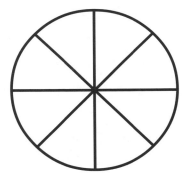

23. Flooding in the Village

500 people are stranded in a flooded village. There is sufficient food for them for 7 days. 200 more people come from a nearby village for shelter. For how many days will the food last now that there are 700 people?

24. What Next?

Look at the figures in the column below. Study the pattern and draw the figure that should come next.

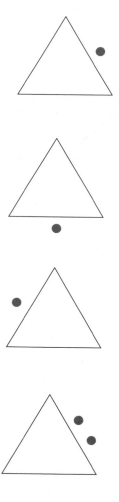

25. Rotten Apples

For every 12 apples that Rachel buys, 3 turn out to be rotten. If Rachel buys 100 apples, how many rotten apples will she have?

26. Guess The Two Numbers

The difference between two numbers is 7. The sum of six times the smaller number and the larger number is 77. What are the two numbers?

27. Star Wonder

Using the numbers 1-12 only once, complete the star below. The numbers in each horizontal and diagonal line of 4 circles must add up to 26.

Think logically to eliminate numbers that will not work.

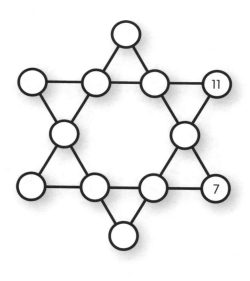

28. Tricky Temperature

What is the difference in temperature between 19°C and - 8°C?

29. Pretty Pie

Given below is a pie chart showing how Sally spent her time last Saturday:

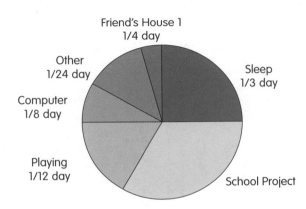

Remembering that there are 24 hours in each day, work out how many hours she spent:
a. Playing
b. On the computer
c. Sleeping

Finally, how much time did Sally spend on her school project?

30. Blue Box and Pink Box

The ratio of the candles in the blue box to the candles in the pink box is 6:11. If 1/3 of the candles from the blue box are put into the pink box, the pink box will have 195 candles. How many candles were there in the blue box to start with?

31. The Mystery of Mary's Age

After 32 years, Mary will be 5 times as old as she was 8 years ago. How old is Mary now?

32. Role Reversal
Which is the smallest 6 digit number which remains the same in value when the order of its digits is reversed?

33. Walkathon
Ridley walks at a speed of 15 km/hr. If he walks for 2 1/2 hours, what is the total distance that he has travelled?

34. Time Flies By
The time now is 01:47 hours. What was the time 2 1/4 hours ago? Give the time using the 24 hour clock.

35. Who Am I?

I am a three digit number.
The first and the last digit are the same.
The sum of my digits is a square.
The product of my digits is a cube.
Who am I?

36. Letters and Digits

Replace the letters with the correct digits:

```
   2 8 7 1
 - A 8 B 1
 ─────────
   1 C 5 0
```

A, B, C will be:

    a. 1,2,0   b. 0,1,2
    c. 2,1,0   d. 1,1,0

Shadow Matching

All Tangled Up!

There are lots of tentacles on this page.
That's because there are too many
octopus shadows!
Can you find the right one?

Face Off!

Hi. Hi. Hi. I have three heads and all of them can talk. But all my heads together cannot find the right shadow.
Will you use your head and help us?

All Clawed Out!

When crabs are scared they scuttle away. This crab is afraid because he can't find his shadow. Can you help him?

Whistle Blower!

Oops! I was having so much fun at the party that I lost my shadow. Which of these could it be?

Bear All!

There is one true shadow that matches
my face. Who will find the shadow first?
Let's have a race!

Spaced Out!

What a silly alien! He can't recognise his own shadow. Show him how clever you are by finding the correct one.

Balancing Act!

I'm so busy balancing the ball on my
nose, I haven't got time to look for my
shadow. Will you find it for me?

Cock - A - Doodle - Who!

Cock a Doodle Doo, what shall I do? If I don't find my shadow, everyone will laugh at me. Can you help?

Winging It!

Some insects have many eyes; some have many wings; others have many legs. This fellow seems to have many shadows! Which is his real one?

53

Making A Point!

The swordfish is quite a unique fish. This one seems more unique than others; it has 5 shadows! Can you fish out the correct one?

Parkside Chat!

Five shadows on this page, but only one
is mine. Can you find the only one that
fits me perfectly fine?

Double Trouble!

Q: Do monsters have 5 shadows?
A: No, they have one like everyone else!
Find the correct one from this group.

It's A Bug's Life

I can't find my shadow. Help me please.
Surely it has to be one of these?

Foxed Or What!

This fox is a cunning and clever animal,
but he still can't find his correct shadow.
Can you help him?

Creepy Crawly!

Insects cannot have 5 shadows, they only have one! Find the correct shadow from these creepy ones below.

Worming Out!

Yummy! What a lovely apple. Now, if I could only find my correct shadow, everything will be perfect!

Visual Illusions

Parallel Or Not?

Are your eyes playing tricks? Look sharp and decide if these lines are parallel or not!

Gender Bender!

Whose picture can you see in this image? Is it a beautiful young lady or a man with a moustache?

Five-Legged Wonder!

Is this elephant so heavy that it has five
legs instead of four? Or are your eyes
playing tricks? Check it out!

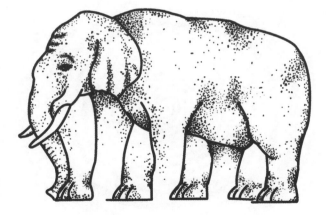

Do A Wheelie!

Stare at the centre of the circle for
30 seconds…is the spiral coiling inward
or growing outward?

Go Dotty!

All you have to do is stare at this grid.
Can you see white dots? Or are they
black? Well, it is for you to decide.

Boxed In?

Are there arrows or white squares on this page? Let your eyes decide!

Let's Face It!

Here is an image of a vase. Or are these the profiles of two people facing each other? Can you tell?

Ball On The Roll!

If you stare long enough at the ball in the center, you will find that it starts to move! Amazing isn't it?

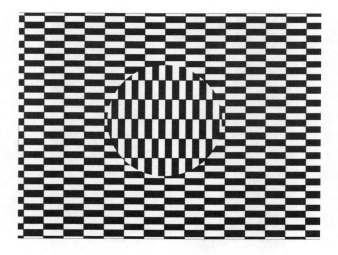

Royal Mounts!

Black horses and riders going right or
white horses and riders going left?

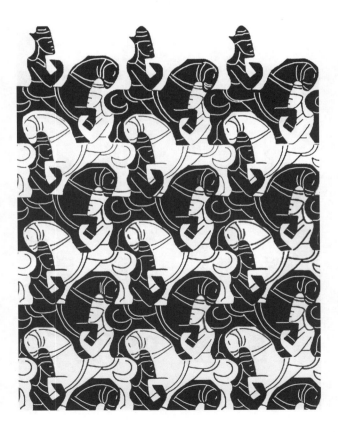

Square Fare!

Do you think this square has straight
lines or are the lines wobbly?
If you look carefully, you should be able
to work it out.

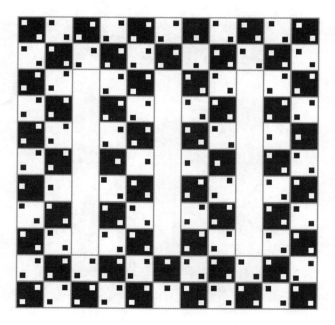

Musician Or Muse?

Do you see a musician or a lady's face?
Rub your eyes and look again to clear
the mystery.

Standing Tall!

Is this a picture of a balcony or is it some women standing? Can you figure out this optical illusion?

Book Blunder!

What's wrong with this book? Is it facing down or is it facing up? You will need to look really hard to try and figure this one out!

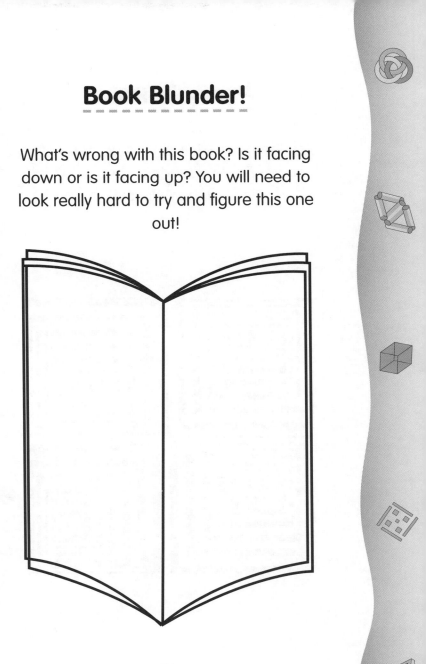

Pyramid Point!

Are the pyramids pointing up or pointing down? That depends on how you look at them. Enjoy!

Size Matters!

Three soldiers in a row standing by a wall. Can you work out which one is the tallest of them all or are they all the same size?

Spot On!

Two circles are placed opposite each other. Can you identify which circle is bigger?

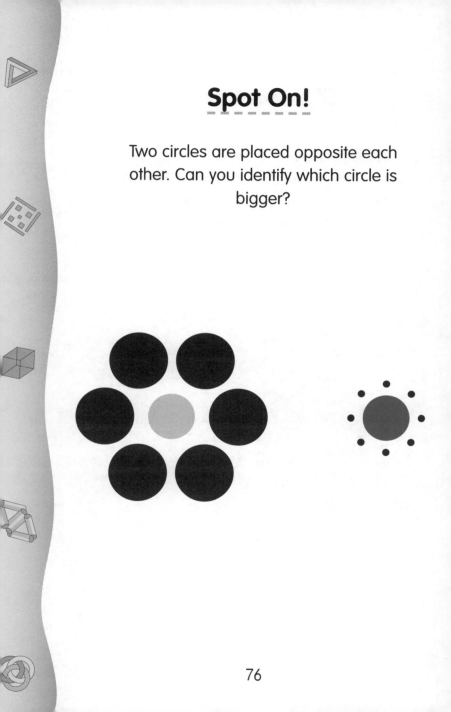

Identical Pairs

Dinosaur Duo!

There are two identical dinosaurs amongst this group. Look carefully at all the images and draw a circle around the two that are exactly the same.

Double Scoops!

There are two identical ice creams in this group. Look carefully at the pictures and draw a circle around the two that look equally delicious!

Tale Of Two Trainers!

Luckily, there is a pair of identical trainers in this group. Look carefully and draw a circle around the proper pair.

Turkey Twins!

There are two identical turkeys on this page.
Circle the ones that are exactly the same.

Double Decker!

Here is a group of double decker buses.
Look carefully and draw a circle around the
two that are the same.

Rose Replicas!

Can you find two identical roses in this group? Circle the two that are the same.

Pizza Pair!

Someone has ordered two pizzas with the same toppings! Draw a circle around the two that are the same.

Similar Skateboards?

There are two identical skateboards in this group. Circle the ones that are the same then do some tricks!

Matching Masks!

There are two identical masks in this group.
Ring the ones that are equally scary!

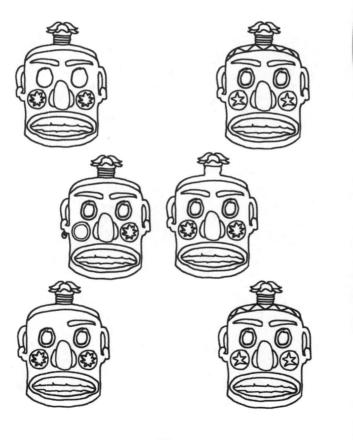

Clone Clowns!

There are two identical clowns in this group.
Look carefully and draw a circle around the
two that are exactly the same.

Hello!

We need two identical cellphones.
Look carefully at this group then draw a
circle around the two that are
exactly the same.

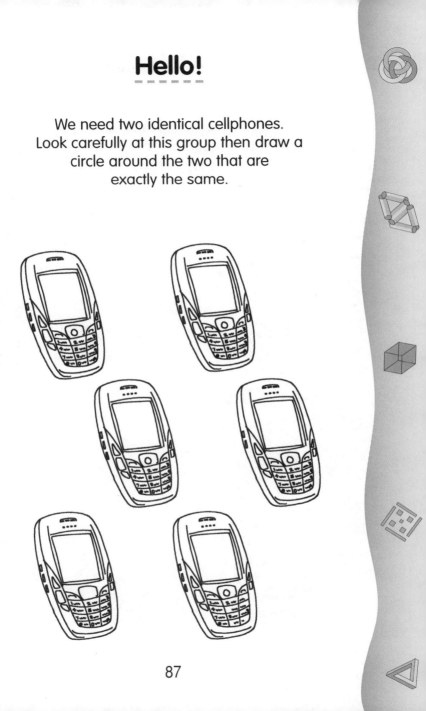

Duckie Duos!

There are two identical ducks in this group.
Draw a circle around the two twins before
they fly away!

Double Beats!

There are two identical drums in this group.
Draw a circle around the same ones so that
we can start a band.

Peas In A Pod!

There are two identical pea pods here.
Look carefully and draw a circle around the
two that are exactly the same.

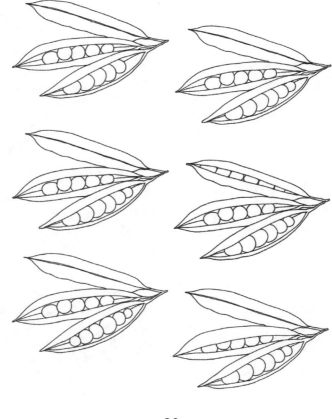

It's A Rerun!

There are two identical television sets in this group. Find the two that are showing the same picture.

Twice The Light!

Two of the solar systems below are the same. Draw a circle around them both.

Can You Find It?

Fancy playing detective? Try to locate all the items mentioned in the list below each picture.

Lost At Sea

1. Anchor
2. Dolphin
3. Turtle
4. Crown
5. Mouse
6. Bow

Goodies For Breakfast

1. Fish
2. Glass of milk
3. Butter dish
4. Cat
5. Newspaper
6. Marmalade

Oh, What A Mess!

1. Spinning top   2. Yo-yo   3. Spider's web
4. Pebbles   5. Envelope   6. Scissors

Sun, Sand and Surf!

1. Starfish
2. Crab
3. Snorkel
4. Ball
5. Shovel
6. Shell

Let's Party!

1. Mask
2. Triangle
3. Pen
4. Butterfly
5. Pan
6. Star

Men At Work

1. Bird
2. Cat
3. Kite
4. Frog
5. Shovel
6. Snail

The Call Of The Wild!

1. Egg
2. Bumble bee
3. Snake
4. Bird
5. Frog
6. Squirrel

Cook Up A Storm!

1. Flower 2. Shopping bag 3. Milk carton
4. Bananas 5. Egg 6. Bell

A Bright Sunny Day!

1. Mouse
4. Paperboat

2. Hut
5. Bird

3. Butterfly
6. Worm

A Day At The Park

1. Skates
2. Shoe
3. Balloon
4. Ice cream cone
5. Hut
6. Squirrel

Out Of tune!

1. Book
2. Flute
3. Watch
4. Cap
5. Trumpet
6. Apple

Brrr, It's Cold Out There!

1. Ice skate   2. Logs   3. Kite
4. Boy   5. Bird   6. Rabbit

It's A Fishy World

1. Seaweed
2. Anchor
3. Wooden log
4. Coin
5. Bottle
6. Treasure chest

Fun At The Fair!

1. Balloon   2. Garbage can   3. Hamburger
4. Flag   5. Cupcake   6. Baby stroller